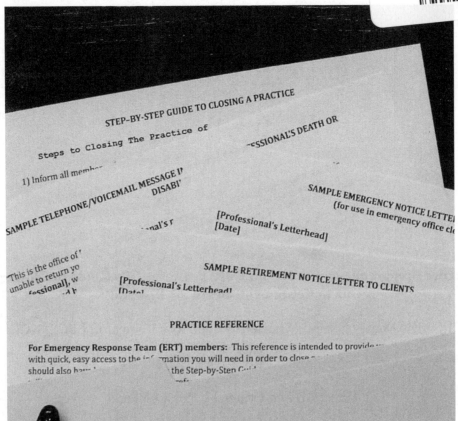

Private Practice Preparedness

The Health Care Professional's Guide to Closing a Practice Due to Retirement, Death, or Disability

Anne Marie "Nancy" Wheeler, JD
Rob Reinhardt, M.Ed., LPCS

Private Practice Preparedness: The Health Care Professional's Guide to Closing a Practice Due to Retirement, Death, or Disability

by Anne Marie "Nancy" Wheeler, JD, and Rob Reinhardt, LPCS, NCC

Edited by S. Kelley Harrell

Cover Art and Design by Rob Reinhardt

ISBN 978-0-9860165-8-5
CreateSpace 1st Edition
A Soul Intent Arts Publication

Soul Intent Arts
www.soulintentarts.com
North Carolina USA

About *Private Practice Preparedness*

Private Practice Preparedness: The Health Care Professional's Guide to Closing a Practice Due to Retirement, Death, or Disability provides the information and tools to ensure a smooth transition of care. Beyond the scope of a personal or professional will, Wheeler and Reinhardt share information, as well as tools to collect and organize such materials. In-depth descriptions of the roles of the Emergency Response Team for closing a practice, their duties, and templates to assist in carrying them out are included. All tools needed for anyone in private practice to respond to an emergency thoroughly and quickly are laid out in this book. Its unique Step-By-Step Guide to closing a practice allows appointed representatives to efficiently take over a practice in an emergency, or as part of a planned transition.

Table of Contents

Acknowledgements

I'd like to thank Rob for his patience, Burt Bertram, Ed.D, LMHC, LMFT and Bernard M. Raiche, J.D., Ed.D., LCSW for their helpful comments, my husband Gary for his support, and my clients of over 30 years for teaching me the importance of good planning. *Nancy*

Thank you, Nancy, for sharing your wealth of knowledge and attention to detail. Thank you, Kelley, Tristan, and Maya for your love and support. *Rob*

About the Authors

Anne Marie "Nancy" Wheeler, JD, is an attorney licensed in Maryland and the District of Columbia. For over 30 years, she has provided risk management consultation services for a major national medical specialty association, and a national association of mental health providers. On a daily basis, she helps practicing psychiatrists, counselors, allied health professionals, and other providers navigate challenging legal, ethical, and regulatory issues ranging from privacy to managed care.

Nancy is also an affiliate faculty member of the Graduate Pastoral Counseling Program of Loyola University Maryland, where she teaches ethics and legal issues courses to masters and doctoral-level students. Additionally, she has presented hundreds of seminars, workshops and keynote addresses nationwide on medical and mental health legal and ethical issues, including closing a professional practice. She has produced newsletters, CDs, video-based programs, and podcasts on legal compliance and risk management strategies. She is the co-author of The Counselor and the Law: A Guide to Legal and Ethical Practice (Alexandria, VA: American Counseling Association, 2007 and 2012) and a contributing author to numerous publications, including "Top Ten Legal and Risk Management Areas of Concern for Psychiatrists," in *Entering Private Practice: A Handbook For Psychiatrists* (ed. J. Lazarus) (American Psychiatric Publishing Inc., 2005).

Nancy has advised numerous professionals considering retirement or closing a private practice. She has also served grieving family members of professionals after the professional's sudden death or disability. Due to the complexity of legal and ethical issues that arise due to lack of planning, on top of the problems for patients and clients, she collaborated with Rob Reinhardt on this user-friendly electronic publication designed to help health care professionals of any age or stage of practice prepare for immediate or eventual closure of a professional practice.

Rob Reinhardt, LPCS, NCC is a Licensed Professional Counselor Supervisor in North Carolina, and a Nationally Certified Counselor. Director of a growing counseling and wellness practice, Serenity Springs Counseling & Wellness, he is also the CEO of Tame Your Practice, a private practice consulting firm. In addition to running a successful practice himself, he helps mental health and other professionals grow their practices, with a focus on efficient and compliant use of technology. Rob is also column editor of the "Tech Tutor" column of *Counseling Today*, the magazine of the American Counseling Association. Prior to entering the world of mental health care, his career focused on Information Technology, with experience in software development, project management, and corporate management.

In talking with Nancy about the need for health care professionals to engage in advanced planning for emergency or planned practice closing, Rob recognized the growing need for documentation of electronic systems. He brings his knowledge of computers and software to this project, in the hopes of easing the burden of transition for professionals and their appointed representatives.

When he isn't talking therapy with clients or technology with health care professionals, Rob can be found playing ultimate frisbee, playing board games, traveling, and/or enjoying time with his family.

Preface

This book discusses the professionals reading it, the people to whom they provide services, and how both are impacted by disruption in services caused by retirement from private practice, as well as emergencies such as death and disability. Some professionals refer to those people as patients, while others call them clients. For the purposes of this book, we use these terms alternately and interchangeably. With regard to gender, alternating pronouns are used.

Throughout this book we use two formats to highlight important information.

> We use this format to point out key points.

> We use this format to provide anecdotes pertinent to the accompanying paragraphs. Some anecdotes are based on real life incidents, though are changed to protect the privacy of individuals involved.

Introduction

> "Professionals of any age must develop plans for their practices in case the unexpected happens."

"Never say die." That expression underscores the western cultural lack of contemplating or planning for death. However, when health care professionals put off dealing with end-of-life issues, it can lead to adverse consequences for loved ones and patients.

> *The physician who was murdered.* As human beings, it's difficult for us to contemplate this possibility. Although it's rare, it happens. Psychiatrists and other mental health professionals are sometimes vulnerable to attacks by very ill patients. I (Nancy) remember my mother telling me about her psychiatrist cousin who was murdered by her own patient several decades ago. This has had a profound effect on me over 30+ years of advising my own mental health and medical clients or their personal representatives after a natural death, or even murder.

However, it's not just eventual death that we must all face. Consider the following statistics:

- A 32-year-old is 6.5 times more likely to experience a serious disability of three months or longer, than they are to die unexpectedly.

- Every 10 seconds someone is injured in an automobile accident.

- Every four seconds someone is injured in any kind of accident. [1]

In short, professionals of any age must develop plans for their practices in case the unexpected happens.

Even those fortunate enough to avoid the pitfalls life might throw our way must consider the future. This group is comprised of people who may have the luxury of planning for eventual retirement, or those who may close or sell their practices to take up new work or pursue other interests. Regardless, none of us can avoid planning for a potential emergency. As soon as we enter professional practice and take on the responsibility of managing care for others, it's time to anticipate the future.

Private Practice Preparedness is intended to help health care professionals plan for the future. Our interest in providing this material stems from our own work–Nancy as a health care attorney, and Rob as a licensed professional counselor and private practice consultant. Nancy's first foray into this topic came almost three decades ago when she handled a frantic call from the spouse of a psychiatrist who died suddenly. That led her to advocate–in writings and seminars—that health care professionals should plan for the possibility of closing a practice, providing for transition of care for patients, and appointing a custodian of records, among other important issues.

In recent years, a number of mental health professionals have advocated use of a "professional will" and an "emergency response team" (often called an "ERT," based on the longstanding concept of such teams, which are part of police, firefighting, or other urgent community response entities). See the following definitions and Annotated References at the end for further information.

While documents like a professional will or Records Custodian Agreement provide basic preparation for the transition of care in case of emergency, this book provides additional insight and tools to ease the burden placed on the caretakers of that process. Furthermore, these tools are also beneficial in voluntary cases of a practice closing, such as retirement or sale of a practice.

> "We encourage readers to seek professional counsel from attorneys, accountants and/or financial advisors about issues related to closing a professional practice."

This book is not intended to provide specific financial or legal advice, but to educate readers about preparation for emergency situations, and to provide resources to prepare for such events. This book and accompanying materials are intended for a broad variety of health care professionals. Where appropriate, templates are provided, and they can be tailored to individual circumstances. For example, a pediatric nurse practitioner may have somewhat different concerns from a psychiatrist so we've designed the materials to be adaptable to the reader's own profession and practice.

Although we give examples of laws and ethics codes that are germane to the topic, we encourage readers to contact their licensure boards and professional associations for further information. We also urge readers to seek professional counsel from attorneys, accountants and/or financial advisors about issues related to closing a professional practice. Particularly with regard to contract templates, professional advice should be sought, as we cannot anticipate all contractual variations, or applicable laws and requirements in existence now or in the future. *This book is intended to aid readers and their counsel, not to substitute for specific legal advice.*

Relevant Entities and Definitions

Before examining the "nuts and bolts" of planning for retirement or emergency, it may be useful to define pertinent terms. These terms are used throughout this book and supplied documents. Understanding them allows for better comprehension of this book, the forms provided with it, and the downloadable documents on our website: www.privatepracticepreparedness.com

Covering Provider(s): Medical or mental health professional(s) who take over the caseload of the primary professional.

Emergency Response Team (ERT): Some health care providers band together in teams to help colleagues, in the event of sudden illness, disability or death. This collective approach can be particularly helpful if a professional has a very busy practice that may be beyond the capability of one "Records Custodian" (defined below) to handle. The team may divide the responsibilities so that one professional handles records requests, another handles appropriate transition of care to a new provider, etc.

Personal Representative: Although this term sometimes has different meanings, in this context it indicates the person appointed by the court, or named in the professional's will, to attend to the deceased person's financial matters. The Personal Representative is a fiduciary who pays debts and distributes assets. If the deceased person created a will, the personal representative is often called an "executor" or "executrix". If a person dies without leaving a will, the Personal Representative is often called an "administrator" or "administratrix.". Some newer laws have eliminated the gender differentiation. Consider this person the business administrator.

Professional Will: Similar in format to a personal will, a professional will is a plan of action that becomes activated in the event that a professional suddenly dies or becomes incapacitated. See Annotated References in this document for further information, including sources for a Professional Will template.

Records Custodian: Caretaker of the records. This person(s) handles requests for clinical records, including requests for direct client access to records. If the primary professional is deceased, the Records Custodian typically works in conjunction with the deceased's personal representative.

Special Administrator: This term may be used in a will to describe someone granted special powers and duties. In some states, this person may function as the Records Custodian, especially if the Special Administrator is licensed similarly to the deceased professional.

HIPAA / HITECH Terms

HIPAA/HITECH: Acronyms for the Health Insurance Portability and Accountability Act and the Health Information Technology for Economic and Clinical Health Act. These federal statutes, with their implementing regulations, govern the security and privacy of Protected Health Information.[2]

Protected Health Information (PHI): Any individually identifiable health information including demographics, medical conditions, or the provision of care. In digital format, referred to as Electronic Protected Health Information (ePHI).

Covered Entity: A term referring to health plans, health care clearinghouses, and health care providers that transmit protected health information electronically. Covered Entities must comply with HIPAA/HITECH laws. For further information, see http://www.cms.gov/Regulations-and-Guidance/HIPAA-Administrative-Simplification/HIPAAGenInfo/AreYouaCoveredEntity.html. Retrieved November 7, 2013.

Business Associate: A person or organization that a covered entity conducts business with, and involves the use or disclosure of protected health information. This role could include a billing agent, software provider, legal representative, or many other possibilities. For further

information, see
http://www.hhs.gov/ocr/privacy/hipaa/understanding/coveredentities/contractprov.html.

Choosing Entities to Make Decisions When We Cannot

Do You Need an ERT?

Whether due to an emergency or part of a plan (i.e., retirement), health care professionals may need to transition care and records of their patients. Likewise, transition of all their business operations to others may need to occur. Whatever the impetus, this transition involves handing decision-making power over to a separate entity.

Depending on the size of the professional practice, built-in coverage may be included, just as it would be if you went on vacation or to a professional conference. This means that other professionals are responsible for the care of your clients while you are out of town. However, it may be important for such a group to have an understanding, confirmed in writing, that coverage is expected in an emergency. For solo or small group practices, this specificity becomes crucial. Establishing a small group of like-minded and similarly licensed professionals who all agree to accept some coverage of duties in the event of an emergency may be a desirable approach. If a professional in the coverage group dies or becomes seriously ill or disabled, the others would pitch in and offer to see patients.

> "Establishing a small group of like-minded and similarly licensed professionals who all agree to accept some coverage of duties in the event of an emergency may be a desirable approach."

However, in some cases, it may be difficult for just one provider, or a loosely affiliated group, to handle requests for records, respond to clients' questions and concerns, and also see patients for treatment or therapy. In such a case, it may be appropriate to have an "Emergency Response Team" (ERT). Such may be the case for a full-time clinician, or one who works for multiple locations/practices. In taking this collective approach, we recommend that the reader expect the worst. Consider the following:

- Should a crisis arise, how many people would it take to immediately contact clients about current appointments and begin to transfer their care?

- Would those same people also be able to handle incoming calls from new patients?

- What about requests for clinical records?

- Would colleagues be willing to do this extra work without remuneration, or should the professional consider offering reasonable payment for the colleagues' time?

A couple of providers may be willing to take on the job of talking to clients. Some providers could agree to cover the practice, taking over the care of the patients or offering appropriate referrals. Another provider might take on the responsibility of transferring records to the client or new provider, and work as a liaison with the family or personal representative of the injured, ill or deceased provider. Whatever the method, consider what is legally required in the state in which the practice is based, and develop appropriate authorization forms, notice to patients, and procedures for handling storage of and requests for records. Along with obtaining appropriate legal advice, contact the appropriate state licensure board and verify relevant ethics codes developed by state professional associations. Also, periodically review emergency planning documents, as changes in the relevant laws and ethics codes are likely in the future.

> "Whatever the method, consider what is legally required in the state in which the practice is based, and develop appropriate authorization forms, notice to patients, and procedures for handling storage of and requests for records."

Advantages of an ERT

> *The physician who left no instructions for emergencies and died suddenly of a heart attack.* The physician's spouse called me, crying and pleading for help. The understandably grieving spouse clearly was not in a position to notify patients. This is a good example of why a trusted professional colleague should be handling calls to patients/clients instead of the personal representative of the deceased, especially since the personal representative of the deceased professional is often a close relative or friend. A spouse, significant other, or very close friend needs time to grieve before becoming involved with ongoing efforts to close the practice.

Professionals often appoint a spouse, significant other, or trusted friend to act as their legal "Personal Representative" in the event of death. While that may seem like the most convenient approach now, remember that such a person may be grief-stricken, and unable to properly handle professional needs. In this case, an Emergency Response Team may be more equipped to respond.

Also, if the Personal Representative isn't familiar with the practice occupation or its legal and ethical requirements, this person should probably not be the one to handle highly sensitive medical or mental health information. It is typically more appropriate, from a legal and ethical standpoint, to have a similarly licensed professional make decisions that could have a clinical impact on clients, or that could lead to a breach of confidentiality or privacy. That said, it is likely that a relative or close friend will be appointed as the Personal Representative in the professional's personal will. We aren't suggesting that the Personal Representative be kept out of the loop; however, advance clarification of the specific duties each person will carry out should be detailed.

> "It is typically more appropriate, from a legal and ethical standpoint, to have a similarly licensed professional make decisions that could have a clinical impact on clients, or that could lead to a breach of confidentiality or privacy."

Establishing and Re-evaluating an ERT

No matter how many people are chosen as part of the ERT, it's important to re-evaluate it on a regular basis. Let's take the case of a group of six proactive Licensed Professional Counselors who agreed to form an ERT several years ago. After 10 years, only two of those counselors are still practicing. It may be time to consider adding members to the group so that there is a fully functioning ERT in the event of an emergency.

Additionally, even though something can happen to a professional of any age, it's logical to form an ERT comprised of similarly licensed professionals of different ages and professional stages. Diversity ensures that the team remains viable and capable of performing its duties without detriment to services or care.

In considering the re-evaluation of an ERT, we recommend checking in with the team once per year to ensure each member is still willing and able to carry out his or her duties, if needed. Written documents should be updated with changes in team membership and instructions. Following are other events that might prompt the re-evaluation of the group:

One of the members:

- Retires

- Stops practicing in the field

- Moves a great distance away

- Takes on additional responsibilities, which might reduce her ability to respond in a timely manner

Along with detailing how to form a supportive ERT, consider being on a colleague's team. Agreeing to serve another professional in need is truly the embodiment of the concept of "aspirational ethics." Serving on an ERT will give insight into what is needed from each role; thus, it can provide ongoing information on how a team should be structured.

In addition to recruiting responsible professionals to handle affairs in case of emergency, it's important that to document items the team must handle. The Personal Representative and/or Emergency Response Team and/or Records Custodian will need to quickly access information and understand exactly what should be done. Ideally, these requirements are well-documented, and proper procedures will have been reviewed with each team member. Having the process documented allows them to respond quickly in the event of emergency, providing continuity of care for patients.

> "In addition to recruiting responsible professionals to handle affairs in case of emergency, it's important that to document items the team must handle."

Special Note—Solo Practitioners

Solo practitioners sometimes experience a feeling of isolation due to a lack of regular contact with other professionals. This isolation can make it more challenging for them to identify potential candidates for an ERT, records custodian or personal representative. We encourage professionals in this situation to reach out to their professional organizations, licensure boards, online professional forums, and local peer networks to establish relationships. Through this relationship building, it is more likely they will be able to establish a mutual agreement with other professional(s) to serve on each other's ERTs.

The following sections provide details and instructions that will help you better understand the process of preparing for emergencies or retirement. Included are explanations of the Practice Reference and other documents that can be provided to a covering provider or ERT.

Handling the Transfer of Records

The format of client records, whether paper or electronic, plays a significant role in how they are handled in the event of disaster. The approaches to securing and protecting them are vastly different as well. Paper records might be protected in locked cabinets inside locked filing rooms. Providing the ERT access to these records is as easy as providing access to a key if an emergency arises. Also inform the Personal Representative about the status of records in the event of emergency, and give him the names, addresses, telephone numbers, and e-mail addresses of each member of the ERT.

> "The format of client records, whether paper or electronic, plays a significant role in how they are handled in the event of disaster. The approaches to securing and protecting them are vastly different as well."

Electronic records often involve encryption, passwords, and multi-factor authentication (e.g., fingerprint recognition). Because of these safeguards, ensuring your ERT has access to these records can be much more complex. In addition, best practices require that you change passwords to sensitive systems on a regular basis. Tracking this information is an important part of your emergency planning process. Additionally, it's possible that members of your ERT are not familiar with the programs that you use. Along with passwords, instructions for accessing your electronic systems and programs should be included in your emergency planning documentation.

Regardless of format, taking over as caretaker of the records is no light-hearted task, as most professional/ethical standards require that records be maintained for a significant amount of time.

> "Along with passwords, instructions for accessing your electronic systems and programs should be included in your emergency planning documentation."

Paper Records

In the case of paper records, transitioning should be straightforward. Getting the records into the hands of the Custodian should be as simple as documenting location(s) of the records and providing the appropriate access tools. These tools may include a set of keys, and possibly an alarm code, if all records are stored at the practice location. For a long-standing practice, there may be record storage facilities involved.

When using a record storage company, it's important to have a clear understanding of how such a transition will take place. With some companies, simple possession of the key and knowledge of the location will suffice. With others, identification may be required, and only the account owner has access. In that scenario, legal documentation noting the right of access as the Records Custodian will be required. Exactly how this transfer will take place and what might be required of the Records Custodian should be documented as part of the emergency planning process.

When dealing with multiple locations, it's important that the Records Custodian have some way to identify where any particular file might be. Since the vast majority of the Custodian's responsibilities involve locating the file for "John Doe", she will be saved significant headaches if she readily knows whether a specific file will be on site (in the office) or in storage.

Furthermore, having a solid organizational system, including clear labeling of file containers, along with solid documentation explaining the system, is imperative.

> "Getting the records into the hands of the Custodian should be as simple as documenting their location(s) and providing the appropriate access tools."

Electronic Records

Increasingly, clinicians store their client information electronically, often in an Electronic Health Record (EHR), Electronic Medical Record (EMR), or Practice Management System. These systems may be traditional software (installed on a local computer/server) or cloud-based (accessed over the Internet). While there is a growing market of "all in one" solutions, some practices may have patient information spread across separate systems for billing, scheduling, and progress notes. Access to any one of these systems may be as simple as a password, or may include multi-factor authentication techniques, like fingerprints or time-sensitive codes generated by third-party applications.

Because of the array of possibilities and potential for complexity, it's important to consider all of the following in completing the documentation for your emergency response team:

- List all devices where client data is stored, maintained, or transmitted (laptops, desktops, tablets, flash drives, smart phones, portable hard drives, etc.).

- List all software programs used to store, maintain, or transmit patient data (accounting software, progress note software, practice management systems, etc.).

- For each program, note what it is used for (billing, notes, scheduling, etc.).

- List all computer files/folders where client information might be saved and/or backed up.

- Make a special note of any files that can/should be destroyed.

- For each device, program, file or folder, note any passwords or other security measures in place, and how to gain access through them.

- Make a special note as to the best resource for patient contact data and where it is located, as well as how to determine whether a client is "active" or "inactive." Some may use the term "current" rather than "active". This refers to those clients who still actively schedule services with the professional. Also, note how to locate patients' last appointments and their next scheduled appointment, if applicable. This information will be important for the Emergency Response Team to access right away.

- For any third party services (billing service, cloud-based software, etc.), note the policies and procedures for accessing the account as a Records Custodian. (See special note below.)

In addition to the templates illustrated later in this book, an additional template for tracking software is available for download to those who have purchased this book at www.privatepracticepreparedness.com

For all of the various electronic devices, files, and programs, it's also important to include detailed instructions on how to use them. For commonly used word processing files, provide a list of location(s). This location will need to include the physical location (e.g. "laptop #4"), as well as the specific location (e.g. "C:\My Documents\Client Data\").

For something complex like an EHR or Practice Management System, it's important to include detailed instructions. These instructions should include how to log in, how to locate patient data, and how to export or send records to another entity, should the need arise. It's also important to note how to contact the support team for that software vendor and how to get training in its use. Since such training can sometimes be extensive, consideration should be given to appointing a Records Custodian who is already familiar with the system(s) being used, or at least is comfortable with technological systems.

> "For something complex like an EHR or Practice Management System, it's important to include detailed instructions."

HIPAA Considerations

If you are a HIPAA Covered Entity[3], the Emergency Response Team should understand what that means so that they can assume that role and remain in compliance. To be clear in that definition, share with them practice-specific HIPAA Policies and Procedures and Notice of Privacy Practices documents. It's also a good idea to document the ERT plan and team members in the HIPAA Privacy and Security Policies, as well as any applicable Informed Consent for clients.

Finally, while many members of an ERT may already be HIPAA Covered Entities, ensure that team members will follow practice-specific HIPAA Privacy and Security Policies. If they're not HIPAA Covered Entities, have them sign a HIPAA Business Associate Agreement. Additionally, have your Personal Representative sign a HIPAA Business Associate Agreement.

Because of the sensitive nature of user names, passwords, and patient data, it's important that such information be secured. One method of security is to encrypt this documentation and store it on a flash drive. That flash drive could then be stored in a safe deposit box, and the decryption password presented in emergency documentation.

> "While many members of an ERT may already be HIPAA Covered Entities, ensure that team members will follow practice-specific HIPAA Privacy and Security Policies."

Third-Party Records Services

Any time a third-party service is used to store records, it's important to address the possibility of catastrophe. Make a note of the vendor's policy regarding access to the account. Points to consider include:

- Can anyone with the password access the account?

- Are there other security measures in place? (e.g., PIN numbers, fingerprint scans, security questions, etc.)

- Will a Records Custodian need to produce legal documentation to gain access?

- Does the vendor need to be informed of that relationship ahead of time?

- Will the account/services still be subject to a fee, or can the account be suspended in a way that allows access to current records, but no creation of new ones?

- Will technical support be willing to provide emergency help/training in the use of the system so that client information can be accessed quickly?

Ownership of the Data

A significant factor to consider is ownership of patient data. Often clinicians are employees or contractors of a larger practice, and the data (paper or electronic) is stored in a shared practice system. It's imperative that clinicians understand their contracts and how this data is handled. Does the practice own the data (and therefore own responsibility of emergency response)? Or does the clinician retain ownership? This factor is often overlooked in professional planning, and has the potential for causing conflict, even in the absence of emergency—when the clinician leaves to practice elsewhere. In the case of catastrophe, the ERT must clearly understand their rights and responsibilities toward the clients and their data.

Billing and Financial Records

When considering the potential transfer of ownership or closure of a business due to retirement, emergency, or death, it is equally important to have clear, accurate financial records. The person taking over the administration of the business must know where the money is (i.e., banking institutions and accounts), what bills need to be paid (i.e., vendors and other contractual obligations), how employees are paid (i.e., payroll responsibilities), and how to bill for services rendered for which payment has not yet been made. Having to figure out all of this in the midst of a crisis takes away valuable time from communication with patients. Even if this information is needed—in a non-emergency situation, such as at the point of retirement or in consideration of a sale of your practice—everything will proceed more smoothly if this information is accurately and well-documented.

> "The person taking over the administration of the business must know where the money is, what bills need to be paid, how employees are paid, and how to bill for services rendered that have not yet been paid for."

Business Technology Considerations

Gone are the days when closing a practice was relatively simple, from a record-keeping standpoint. What happens to all those online accounts? Most professionals have user IDs and passwords for their licensure boards, bank accounts, professional associations, social media accounts, business telephones, cell phone accounts, Internet service, etc. Keep a list of these user IDs and passwords, but do not email it to the Personal Representative, Records Custodian and/or Emergency Response Team unless you are certain such email is secure/encrypted from end to end! These login credentials may be listed on the "Practice Reference" (see below) if this checklist is kept in a secure place with instructions regarding accessing it in the event of emergency.

Another option is to create a list of all online accounts, user IDs, and passwords, then store them in an encrypted online password management file or program. These online password managers securely encrypt and store your passwords online, allowing you to access them all through one master username and password. Then only one username and password needs to be kept secure and transferred in the event of death or incapacity. As with your use of any technology, it is recommended that you also have a backup plan.

> "Another option is to create a list of all online accounts, user IDs and passwords and store them in an encrypted online password management file or program."

When You Have the Option to Choose

> *The mental health therapist who made a quick decision to close his practice, notified clients, then decided he really wasn't ready to retire.* Professionals contemplating retirement and/or closing a practice should take time to think through all the issues and make plans for what comes next. Although the therapist was able to "re-notify" clients that the practice would remain open, he lost existing clients and some may have questioned his motivation for making the decisions without first thinking through the consequences.

Different considerations apply with the luxury of choice, when closing a practice is not due to death, disability or other forced action, such as license suspension or bankruptcy. Job change or election to retire on your own terms may be possibilities. Another possibility is debilitating illness—one that does not always create an emergency, though provides the impetus to close a health care practice.

When making the decision to retire, people generally focus on the monetary issues, and whether they'll have enough money to carry them through their lifespans. However, there are other issues that come into play, such as emotional readiness. See the Annotated Resources for more information on both financial and non-financial considerations involved in the retirement decision.

Related Personal Legal Issues

Consider having a local attorney draft both a personal will and professional will. The latter may explain professional responsibilities and name the Records Custodian, Special Administrator and/or Emergency Response Team, depending on the law and licensure requirements of the residing state. See Bradley et al, in Annotated References in this document for further information, including a Professional Will template.

> "Consider having a local attorney draft both a personal will and professional will. "

The personal will may cross-reference the professional will. Additionally, it would be the right time to consider a "living will," "durable health care power of attorney," and other forms typically included in the umbrella term, "advance directives." These directives are dependent on state law considerations.

Sometimes, forms for such advance directives can be found on the web site of the residing state's Attorney General's Office. For example, Maryland has user-friendly advance directives, including "do not resuscitate" orders and organ donation forms, on its web site, http://www.oag.state.md.us/Healthpol/adirective.pdf.

Special Considerations

Client Records/Record Retention

An important consideration in planning for unforeseen circumstances is to understand and document legal and ethical requirements regarding retention of patient records. First, seek advice from a local health care attorney regarding how long to keep records. Whereas most states don't require counselors, physicians, psychologists, social workers, nurse practitioners, and other health care professionals to keep adult clients' records longer than seven years, it may be advisable for anyone receiving Medicare, Medicaid, or other federal program reimbursement to keep records of adult patients at least ten years past the last date of treatment. (Ten years is the longest time past date of violation that a false claims action may be brought by the federal government against a provider.)

With the treatment of minors, consider keeping records for at least the statutory minimum period or, if it's not addressed by law, at least three years past the date the client reaches the age of majority (which is 18 years of age in most states). Some attorneys advise keeping records indefinitely, but health care providers must balance the possible need for records with the cost and trouble of storing them. In the event of retiring from a group practice, it is acceptable for the group to retain records, though patients should be informed of how they can obtain copies, and how records will be properly stored to comply with state law and HIPAA, as applicable.

> "Some attorneys advise keeping records indefinitely, though health care providers must balance the possible need for records with the cost and trouble of storing them."

Another consideration in setting a record-retention policy is that licensure board investigations may sometimes be brought years after an alleged practice violation. There is often no statute of limitations that applies in this venue, so complaints may be lodged many years after an alleged violation. Documentation of care provided can frequently help a professional's defense attorney get the board complaint dismissed.

Ultimately, there is no "one size fits all" answer to the question of how long to keep records. With careful consideration to the information above, and advice from one's attorney, malpractice company, and state licensure board, a best-case scenario can be created to fit the unique practice.

Regarding destruction of records, paper records should be destroyed by shredding. "Cross-shredding" is advisable if any protected health information is still visible after shredding. To keep track of which records have been destroyed and when, keep a list (log or spreadsheet) of patients/clients by name, date of birth, dates of treatment (which typically may be a to/from range of treatment dates), and date of record destruction.

Electronic records are another matter. Do not assume that "deleting" a file causes it to disappear from a computer. Talk to a tech expert about the options for destruction of files, encryption and/or "degaussing" magnetic storage media.

Third Party Notices

If the practice has employees, remember to notify them regarding practice closure. This notification should be done immediately, usually right before notifying patients, and definitely before the information becomes public. Also notify professional colleagues, insurance companies, licensure board(s), professional associations, managed care entities with which there are binding contracts, and other parties as set forth in the "Practice Documents, Clinical Records & Procedures Checklist" and the "Step-by-Step" checklist below.

> "If the practice has employees, remember to notify them regarding practice closure. This should be done immediately."

Business Format Structure

Depending on the legal structure of the professional practice, steps may need to be taken to dissolve the entity or transfer ownership. Before this becomes a problem, check existing agreements and documents to ensure that the eventuality of death or disability has been contemplated.

Depending on the nature and viability of the practice, you may consider selling the practice to provide revenue for the personal estate. Hiring an employee to take over the practice may be an option. Tangible assets, accounts receivable and goodwill are typically valued to determine fair market value. However, there are important legal and ethical issues, particularly privacy, fee-splitting, and federal and state fraud and abuse laws, which should be evaluated by a local attorney. It's also helpful to involve an accountant or other financial expert to place a value on the practice.

> "Depending on the legal structure of the professional practice, steps may need to be taken to dissolve the entity or transfer ownership.

Impact on Clients

It's important to note that the death or retirement of a trusted provider may have more than just a logistical/practical impact on patients. While especially true for mental health therapists, it can also be the case that a patient may form strong relationships with other professionals. It's important that the ERT involved with contacting these patients understands this dynamic and be prepared to deal with the varied reactions likely to be encountered. Trained staff should be available to help clients deal with the difficult emotions associated with grief and loss. Non-therapy practices may consider partnering with mental health professionals with grief, bereavement, and crisis training as part of their ERT.

> "It's important to note that the death or retirement of a trusted provider may have more than just a logistical/practical impact on patients."

Resources

This section contains templates that can be modified and tailored to each unique practice, and should be reviewed and edited by a local attorney to make sure the information complies with applicable law. Brackets are used to indicate either: 1) information that should be personally inserted; or 2) suggestions to consider. Note that the Step-by-Step Guide to Closing a Practice document described above refers directly to these resources.

Important: These templates are available for download and modification after the purchase of this book, at: http://www.privatepracticepreparedness.com/ While we have presented them here as a reference, they are intended to be downloaded and completed with individual practice information. They can then be provided to the ERT in the case of an emergency. Alternatively, they will make the process of selling or closing a practice much easier should that situation arise in the future. If they require no customization for your practice, some of these templates may be completed within the book itself.

> "After completing all of these documents, they can be kept in a safe place where the ERT can quickly access them."

Following is a brief description of each document in the suggested order of completion. By completing them in this order, we feel you will best understand their purpose and intended use in case of emergency or planned practice closure:

- **Practice Reference**—This document is the heart of the practice-closing process. In addition, it's invaluable in keeping important practice information organized, allowing for efficient access on a daily basis. When completed, it should include all of the information an ERT needs to close the practice. The Step-by-Step Guide to Closing a Practice walks the ERT through the process while referring to the information in the Practice Reference.

- **Records Custodian Agreement**—During the process of completing the Practice Reference, a member of the ERT should be identified as the Records Custodian. Because of the nature of custodial responsibilities, it is important to establish a Records Custodian Agreement with the individual. We recommend having an attorney review the template and make changes to comply with applicable state and federal law and conform to unique needs.

- **Sample Retirement Notice to Patients/Clients**—This letter serves as a template for the ERT to use in the event of emergency or when planning a practice closing. Having it thoughtfully composed in advance allows thorough coverage of details and information.

- **Sample Notice Letter to Patients/Clients**—This template is designed for use in the case of emergency, such as death or disability. Having this completed in advance allows the ERT to respond quickly.

- **Sample Telephone Message**—This template gives the ERT a script for the outgoing voicemail message, in the case of emergency.

- **Step-by-Step Guide to Closing a Practice**—This document is intended to walk the ERT (or the professional, in the case of retirement) through the process of closing the practice. By following the steps and cross-referencing the Practice Reference, the process can be efficient. Modify this document to add or remove steps as needed, or to change their order. When doing so, be mindful that the cross-citations to the Practice Reference are still accurate.

After completing all of these documents, they can be kept in a safe place where the ERT can quickly access them. Alternatively, supply the ERT with a copy for safe- keeping. If you provide them such an "advance copy," ensure that you later provide them with any updates. When organizing documents for the ERT, we recommend placing them in the following order:

1. Step-by-Step Guidelines

2. Practice Reference

3. Sample Telephone Message

4. Sample Notice Letter

5. Records Custodian Agreement

Practice Reference Instructions

The Practice Reference is the core document for your preparedness. Once completed, it will contain all of the information an ERT will need in order to carry out its duties. This reference will provide the ERT with quick access to the information pertinent to the administration of the practice. This reference may also be a current valuable aid to the professional or staff to quickly locate a file or business information.

Note that the Practice Reference is organized in a way that it will work smoothly with the Step-by-Step Guide to Closing a Practice. Specifically, the information in the Practice Reference is in the order it is encountered in the Step-by-Step Guide. This order was preserved to allow an ERT member to quickly and easily follow the Step-by-Step Guide and access information in an emergency.

Following these instructions is a copy of the detailed Practice Reference. Additionally, it is available for download and modification at http://www.privatepracticepreparedness.com/, after purchasing this book. Detailed instructions and other suggestions are included here. They are not included in the downloaded form in order to keep it clean and easy to read.

> "Note that the Practice Reference is organized in a way that it will work smoothly with the Step-by-Step Guide to Closing a Practice. Specifically, the information in the Practice Reference is in the order it is encountered in the Step by Step Guide."

When completing the template, be sure to include any instructions that are personal to the practice setting. Suggested instructions (in italics) are already included in this document.

Consider separating the financial information from the practice management information, to make sure that the right people have access to the right information. For instance, the accountant and personal representative should have access to the financial information, while the Records Custodian and/or Emergency Response or Covering Providers have access to the clinical and records information, as needed. This can be accomplished by printing certain pages and creating packets for each role on the support team.

Important Tips

- Many of the following items require documenting location so they can be readily accessed. We strongly encourage that, when possible, tangible items like documents and keys should be stored in the minimum number of locations possible. This limitation provides additional ease of access in case of emergency. Storage locations for sensitive items and documents should be secure.

- It's possible to have more than one instance of specific items listed below. In such cases, we recommend duplicating items where needed. For example, if the practice has more than one credit card account, duplicate the "Credit Card Account" paragraph for each credit card in possession.

- Sections are labeled with a letter to enable cross-referencing with the Step-by-Step Guide, corresponding to the order in which the items appear on the form. Be sure to consider this order in any modifications made to the template.

Specific Instructions/Guidance (based on section)

A. Emergency Response Team

Role—Note which member of the ERT will fulfill a specific role (e.g., Records Custodian, Personal Representative, etc.). Also make special note of specific tasks for which each individual is responsible (e.g., contacting managed care organizations).

B. Professional Network

Covering Provider—A Covering Provider is someone who is tasked with providing services to the professional's patients should the professional be absent from the office for any reason.

Professionals to Whom You Refer—In addition to the covering provider(s), these are professionals (M.D.s, therapists, APRNs, etc.) to whom clients can be referred.

Others in Referral Network—Note here any providers from whom referrals have been received, who might not otherwise be listed in the "Refer Patients to These Providers" section. These are professionals, agencies, etc., who would need to be informed so they no longer refer to the practice.

C. Telephones and Calling Procedures

Telephone Instructions—Include land and mobile lines. Include information on how to access and/or change messages, and a reminder to discontinue service after leaving it for 3-6 months following practice closure. See "Sample Telephone/Voicemail Message in Event of Professional's Disability or Death" in the Resources section.

E. Records

Client Contact Information—Records include the location of patient contact information. This information may be crucial in providing notice. Lists of past clients (at least two years, or longer if required by state law) should also be accessible for notice purposes.

Retention of Records—Provide instructions for the Records Custodian and Personal Representative regarding record retention requirements/guidelines.

Locating Active Patients—Provide specific instructions here regarding the most efficient way to access or generate a list of currently active clients. These instructions are especially important in case of emergency. (See endnote 4 regarding active patients.)

Computerized Record Information—Note here if patient records are stored in a software solution. Also note the location, whether it is a local server, cloud server, Practice Management System, etc. Make sure protected health information is erased from hard drives after appropriate information is stored safely for required time periods.

Note that HIPAA and state law may protect information in computer records as well as paper records. Passwords should not be shared after death or disability except as needed by a qualified records custodian or administrator. Sharing protected health information with attorneys, accountants or providers who are not covered entities may call for execution of a HIPAA "business associate contract" if they are not a regular part of your workforce (i.e. employees of the company you own or work for).

Psychotherapy Notes—If applicable and kept separate from the rest of the medical record, special protection is given under HIPAA; some states have similar protection for Personal Notes. See 45 C.F.R. § 164.501 for the definition of "psychotherapy notes."

Special Instructions—Ensure that this section also provides instructions to the Covering Provider/Special Administrator/Records Custodian. For example, the following language could be used: "Make sure clients who have appointments listed within the week following my disability or death are called before they show up in the office; please give them an opportunity to process the loss with an appropriate mental health provider."

Be sure to include detailed instructions for accessing records kept in a storage facility. This should include not only how to locate and access the records, but any documentation that will be required of the Records Custodian accessing them.

Important Tip

For complex situations involving multiple computers, software, or systems, refer to the Technology Quick Reference spreadsheet, available to purchasers of this book at http://www.privatepracticepreparedness.com/

F. Educational Institutions

Role—The role would be the service or position the professional fulfills at the institution. It may be helpful to include the role or position of the contact person.

G. Vendors

Vendors might include Internet Service Providers, billing agents, web hosting companies, advertising firms and more.

H. Insurance (managed care and others)

Type—Type may include "MCO" (managed care organization), "EAP" (employee assistance program), or any other organization that provides reimbursement for services.

I. Licensure

License—Be sure to include both the name and number(s) of the professional's license(s).

Locale(s)—Denote the county, state, or country of licensure.

L. Insurance (professional and personal)

Some insurance policies may be physically located in the professional's home. Instruct the Records Custodian/ Special Administrator regarding the location of documents in the event of death, disability or incapacity. Ensure that the administrator of the estate, along with the spouse or partner (if relevant), know where to locate the will and advance directives.

N. Bank and Financial Accounts

Type—Indicate the type of account (e.g. Checking, Savings, Credit Card, etc.)

O. Keys to Office, etc.

Location—Location might be a physical location (office) or item (black filing cabinet).

P. Email

Confidentiality and Privacy—Be sure to note any specific instructions for following HIPAA and state laws regarding email.

Q. Office Policies and Procedures

Office Operating Procedures—Include duties and tasks of any employees in the practice. Employees may be able to help detail the activities. This information may need to be set forth in a separate manual.

R. Office Supplies and Equipment

Equipment—This section might include photocopiers, fax machines, etc. Include maintenance, warranty, and repair records for individual pieces of equipment.

Supplies—These items may include prescription pads and other general office supplies. Attention should be paid to essential items and those that are delivered on a regular basis.

Cross-reference both items to the Vendors section (Section G)

S. Resources

Resources may include any information important in carrying out practice services, administration of the office, or closing the business. This may include ethics codes, state laws, research papers, etc.

Location—The location may be a web site, particularly for items such as ethics codes.

V. Web Site

Web Host—This entity is the vendor that provides web hosting services to the professional.

Web Maintenance Contact—This entity is the vendor who helps maintain and/or edit the website on an ongoing basis.

Instructions—Provide instructions on how to access passwords, edit the web site, etc. If desired, stipulate what the website should say in the event of a closing or emergency. Cross-reference the Vendors section, if needed.

W. Other Projects

Many professionals have other projects, such as continuing education, publications, or other employment. Use this section to note any such items that will require attention or management and any appropriate information or instructions.

X. Other Information

In this section, list anything that wasn't covered elsewhere.

Practice Reference

Reminder: You may have multiple specific items below (e.g. ERT members, credit cards, etc.). In such cases, we recommend duplicating items where needed. Note that this form is organized in a way to work well with the Step-by-Step Guide to Closing a Practice. If you change the order of any items in this reference, be sure to make complementary adjustments in the Step-by-Step Guide.

For Emergency Response Team (ERT) members: This reference is intended to provide you with quick, easy access to the information you will need in order to close a private practice. You should also have been provided with the Step-by-Step Guide to Closing a Private Practice, which will take you through the process and refer to this document.

A. Emergency Response Team (ERT)

Name: _____

Address: _____

Phone (Type): _____

Alt. Phone (Type): _____

Email: _____

Roles: _____

B. Professional Network (Business and Practice Consultants and Referrals)

Covering Providers

Name: _____

Address: _____

Phone (Type): _____

Alt. Phone (Type): _____

Email: _____

Roles: _____

Refer Patients to These Providers

Name: _____

Address: _____

Phone (Type): _____

Alt. Phone (Type): _____

Email: _____

License/Certification: _____

Others In Referral Network

Name: _____

Address: _____

Phone (Type): _____

Alt. Phone (Type): _____

Email: _____

License/Certification: _____

Supervisees

Name: _____

Address: _____

Phone (Type): _____

Alt. Phone (Type): _____

Email: _____

Professional Liability Insurance Risk Manager

Name: _____

Address: _____

Phone (Type): _____

Alt. Phone (Type): _____

Email: _____

Company: _____

Accountant

Name: _____

Address: _____

Phone (Type): _____

Alt. Phone (Type): _____

Email: _____

Company: _____

Attorney

Name: _____

Address: _____

Phone (Type): _____

Alt. Phone (Type): _____

Email: _____

Company: _____

Computer Specialist

Name: _____

Address: _____

Phone (Type): _____

Alt. Phone (Type): _____

Email: _____

Company: _____

Insurance Company or Broker

Name: _____

Address: _____

Phone (Type): _____

Alt. Phone (Type): _____

Email: _____

Company: _____

Other (specify)

Role: _____

Name: _____

Address: _____

Phone (Type): _____

Alt. Phone (Type): _____

Email: _____

Company: _____

C. Telephones and Calling Procedures

Phone Number

Number: _____

Type: _____

Office: _____

Vendor/Acct #: _____

Instructions: _____

_____

_____

Fax Number

Number: _____

Type: _____

Office: _____

Vendor/Acct #: _____

Instructions: _____

_____

_____

Additional Telephone Procedure after Practice Termination:

_____

_____

_____

D. Business Records

Location of Employee Records: _____

Location of Receipts: _____

Location of Tax Forms: _____

Location of Information on Accounts Receivable/Payable: _____

_____

Location of Contracts: _____

Location of Petty Cash Fund: _____

Location of Asset Information: _____

_____

_____

E. Records (Clinical and Related)

Location(s)

Client Demographic Data: _____

Calendar/Schedule: _____

Clinical Record: _____

Other (Identify): _____

Retention of Records: _____

_____

_____

_____

How to Locate Active patients (cross reference Endnote 4 in Private Practice

Preparedness): _____

_____

_____

_____

_____

_____

Computerized Record Information

Type of Data: _____

Location: _____

Computer(s)

Computer: _____

Type: _____

Location: _____

Password: _____

Psychotherapy Notes (if applicable)

Location: _____

Informed Consent Documents/ Authorizations, etc.

Location: _____

Special Instructions for Records

_____

_____

_____

_____

F. Educational Institutions

Institution: _____

Role: _____

Contact Person: _____

Phone: _____

Alt. Phone: _____

Email: _____

G. Vendors

Vendor: _____

Type/Service: _____

Acct #: _____

Contact Person: _____

Contact Number: _____

Contact Email: _____

Instructions:

_____

_____

_____

_____

H. Insurance (Managed Care and Other Contractual Agreements)

Organization: _____

Type/Service: _____

Acct #: _____

Contact Person: _____

Contact Number: _____

Contact Email: _____

Instructions: _____

_____

_____

_____

Location of contracts: _____

I. Licensure

License Number: _____

Jurisdiction: _____

Licensing Board: _____

Contact Person: _____

Contact Number: _____

Contact Email: _____

Instructions: _____

_____

_____

_____

J. Professional Associations

Organization: _____

Acct/Member #: _____

Contact Person: _____

Contact Number: _____

Contact Email: _____

Instructions: _____

_____

_____

_____

K. Professional Identifiers

National Provider Identifier (NPI): _____

Council for Affordable Quality Healthcare (CAQH ID): _____

L. Insurance (Personal and Business/Professional)

Professional Liability (Malpractice) Insurance

Policy No.: _____ Issued by: _____

Telephone Number: _____

Address of Carrier: _____

Location of Policy: _____

Renewal Date: _____

Operating Procedure: _____

Procedure upon termination of practice: call to notify carrier and keep policy in effect for approximately one calendar quarter while wrapping up practice and to allow for questions and record transfer. If policy is "claims made" instead of "occurrence," obtain tail coverage (extended reporting period coverage).

Disability Insurance (Long Term)

Policy No.: _____ Issued by: _____

Telephone Number: _____

Address of Carrier: _____

Location of Policy: _____

Renewal Date: _____

In event of death, cancel policy so that estate is not billed for premiums. Check with carrier and attorney to see if policy must be kept in force while clients are being referred and requests for records are being handled. In the event of disability, notify carrier immediately so that coverage may begin in accordance with policy.

Disability Insurance (Short Term)

Policy No.: _____ Issued by: _____

Telephone Number: _____

Address of Carrier: _____

Location of Policy: _____

Renewal Date: _____

Procedure upon termination of practice or death: notify carrier immediately and cancel policy so that professional or estate is not billed for premiums. In the event of disability, notify carrier immediately so that coverage may begin in accordance with policy.

Health Insurance

Policy No.: _____ Issued by: _____

Telephone Number: _____

Address of Carrier: _____

Location of Policy: _____

Renewal Date: _____

Secondary Policy No.: _____ Issued by: _____

Telephone Number: _____

Address of Carrier: _____

Location of Policy:_____

Renewal Date: _____

Notify health insurance carrier immediately in event of death. If spouse or other persons are covered under the same policy, make sure they have the opportunity to have coverage extended or obtained elsewhere before terminating policy. If Medicare eligible, make appropriate notifications. MediGap or other supplementary and Medicare Part D coverage should also be listed, if applicable.

Long Term Care Insurance

Policy No.: _____ Issued by: _____

Telephone Number: _____

Address of Carrier: _____

Location of Policy: _____

Renewal Date: _____

Notify insurance carrier immediately in event of death. In the event of disability or illness, make sure premiums are continued and check into benefits which may be immediately available.

Other Insurance (this might include office overhead insurance, general liability insurance, business interruption insurance, premises insurance, renter's insurance, umbrella insurance, etc.)

Type: _____

Policy No.: _____ Issued by: _____

Location of Policy: _____

Ascertain whether coverage should be terminated and notify insurance carrier.

M. Leases

Office Lease

Name, Address, Phone Number and E-mail Address of Landlord:

_____

_____

_____

Expiration of Term and Notice Requirements: _____

_____

Location of Office Lease: _____

_____

_____

Check terms of lease and notify landlord.

Equipment Lease(s)

Type: _____

Expiration of Term and Notice Requirements: _____

_____

Location of Leases: _____

Check terms of lease(s) and provide appropriate notice of termination.

Office/Space Sharing Agreements

Location of Agreements: _____

Details and Instructions: _____

_____

Check contractual agreements and notify other therapists in a shared office arrangement.

N. Bank and Financial Accounts

Bank Accounts

Type: _____

Account Number: _____

Bank: _____

Location of Checkbook and/or Statements: _____

Other Information: _____

_____

Safe Deposit Box Number: _____

Bank (and Branch): _____

Location of Key: _____

Close bank accounts only after all billing and deposit actions have been concluded and statements reconciled.

Retirement Account(s)

Type of Account (e.g., SEP-IRA, 401(k) etc.): _____

Account No.: _____

Bank or Financial Services Company: _____

Location of Documents: _____

Notify retirement plan administrator, if applicable, of practice closure. If you have employees, check with administrator and/or attorney regarding notice and action to be taken. Special rules may apply to trustee-directed plans.

O. Keys to Office, File Cabinets, Safe, etc.

Location: _____

Location of Keys: _____

Instructions re/ use of keys, codes, combinations, etc.: _____

_____

_____

P. Mail and Related Services

U.S. Mail ("Snail Mail")

Location: _____

Procedures for Outgoing and Incoming Mail (including acting on information needed in timely fashion for patient care and use of certified mail):

_____

_____

_____

Instructions for Canceling Mail Service (after payables and receivables are handled):

_____

_____

_____

E-mail

Confidentiality and Privacy Notes/Requirements (x-ref. HIPAA and state law procedures):

_____

_____

Rules for Deleting (check with attorney and/or state licensure board(s)):

_____

_____

_____

Signatures: _____

_____

Other Express Carrier Service

Name of Company (e.g., FedEx or UPS): _____

Location of Account Information: _____

Q. Office Policies and Procedures

HIPAA Policies and Procedures (location) _____

_____

Billing Procedures (location) _____

Employment Procedures and Employee Manual (location) _____

_____

Office Operating Procedures _____

_____

_____

_____

R. Office Supplies and Equipment

Equipment: _____

Location: _____

Type/Service: _____

Acct #: _____

Contact Person: _____

Contact Number: _____

Contact Email: _____

Approval Process: _____

Instructions/Information:_____

_____

_____

Supplies: _____

Location: _____

Supplier: _____

S. Resources

Ethics Codes/ Relevant Laws Summaries, etc.

Resource: _____

Location: _____

T. Staff Privileges or Other Institutional Affiliations

Location of Information: _____

Instructions: _____

U. Tax Issues

Location of files: _____

_____

_____

V. Website and E-Mail

Domain Name: _____

Web Host: _____

Web Maintenance Contact: _____

Instructions: _____

_____

_____

_____

W. Other Projects

Project: _____

Instructions: _____

X. Other Information and Instructions:

_____

_____

_____

_____

_____

Records Custodian Agreement

This document is intended as a template to aid the Professional and her local attorney draft an agreement between the Professional and Records Custodian. A local attorney should be consulted due to differences in state law. Examples and notes for consideration are in italics.

This Agreement (the "Agreement") is made and effective this ___ day of _____, 20__, by and between _____ [name of professional or, if deceased, Personal Representative of Professional's estate] (hereinafter called "Professional") and _____ [name of records custodian] (hereinafter called "Records Custodian").

Statement of Background Information [*optional; your attorney may wish to include information that pertains to your unique situation*].

   A. Professional seeks assistance from Records Custodian in handling requests for records and storing such records in the event of Professional's death, disability or other incapacity. Records Custodian understands that his/her name and contact information have been furnished to patients/clients through Professional's written informed consent document [*and to the appropriate licensure board, if required by state law*].

   B. Records Custodian has agreed to receive and respond appropriately to requests for patient/client records in accordance with state and federal law, including HIPAA.

   C. [*Insert any other relevant background information. For example, if an Emergency Response Team has been created to deal with issues such as notice to patients/clients and transition of care, this might be specified here in order to distinguish the exact duties of the Records Custodian from the rest of the Team.*]

Now, therefore, in consideration of the mutual promises and conditions set forth herein, and other valid consideration, the parties hereby agree as follows:

1.0 Duties of Professional [or Personal Representative, Acting on Behalf of (*insert name of Professional*)

   1.1. **Notice.** Professional, or his/her Personal Representative in conjunction with the Records Custodian, will provide notice of office closure or Professional's death, disability, etc. to Professional's employees as soon as possible after the event triggering the need for notice. Professional, or his/her Personal Representative in conjunction with the Records Custodian [*or designated employee, if applicable*], will send a written notice to all patients/clients of Professional treated within three (3) years of last date of practice [check state law to see if time frame is different], or to those patients'/clients' parents or guardians, stating that Professional's office will be closed effective [*fill in date, which will probably be at least 90 days from notice date*] and that any future inquiries regarding records will be handled by [*fill in either Professional or Records Custodian*]. [*Note that the wording of this section* *will change, depending on the circumstances. For example, if Professional is healthy at the time of retirement and/or closing a practice, the Professional should send the written letter to patients/clients. However, if the practice is closed due to sudden illness, disability or death, the Personal Representative and/or Records Custodian may send the written notice. Also, contact information for the Records Custodian in the notice should include his/her address, telephone number and e-mail address.]*

1.2. **Voicemail**. Professional, or his/her Personal Representative if Professional is unavailable, will include contact information (address, telephone number and e-mail address) for the Records Custodian on the voicemail of the Professional's office telephone number (and website, if applicable). The message will state the effective office closure date and that Records Custodian will handle any future inquiries regarding records. The Professional, or his/her Personal Representative, will ensure that the telephone number and voicemail message will remain operational for at least [*fill in time; six months is recommended unless state law specifies otherwise*] after notice is given to patients/clients.

1.3. **Training of Records Custodian's Staff** [*if applicable; this may also be done by Records Custodian and such duties could be set forth in section 2 of this agreement*]. Professional, Personal Representative or his/her designee will train Record Custodian's staff in the procedure for receiving, processing, and documenting the disposition of record requests.

1.4. **Records Storage Company** [*if applicable; sometimes Records Custodian will store records at his/her own office*]. Professional or Personal Representative will arrange for storage of records by [specify records storage company, which may include electronic records storage company] and will be responsible for payment of fees. Records will be maintained for a period of [*fill in appropriate time frames; see considerations listed in accompanying electronic document on "Handling the Transfer of Records"*].

2.0 Duties of Records Custodian

2.1 **Processing Records Requests**. Records Custodian shall advise any callers seeking records to submit requests to Records Custodian in writing. Records Custodian shall not verify by telephone whether or not any particular person was a patient/client of Professional without proper written authorization. After appropriate review, and when consistent with section 2.3 of this Agreement, Records Custodian shall provide copies of records to the appropriate party within [   ] days [*fill in blank; although HIPAA may allow up to 30 days, state law should be ascertained because some states require release within a shorter time period*]. The method for sending records will be determined in accordance with federal and state law. [*In some circumstances, you may wish to send paper records by certified mail with tracking. Check both state law and HIPAA, because if a patient/client requests that copies of* *electronic records be sent electronically, you may have to comply with that request.*] The Records Custodian shall maintain the written request for information in the patient's/client's record, with appropriate documentation of how the request was handled (e.g., copy of cover letter that accompanied release of records, along with tracking or other proof that information was sent).

2.2 **Other Requests, including Legal Documents**. If Records Custodian receives any subpoenas, court orders, legal papers or requests for information or records from any persons pertaining to treatment or treatment records of Professional, Records Custodian shall immediately notify Professional [*or Personal Representative,` if appropriate*] at [*insert telephone number*] and shall make arrangements to forward any written communication to Professional [*or Personal Representative*] in a timely manner, as required by law.

2.3 **Legal and Ethical Requirements**. Records Custodian shall comply with all applicable state and federal laws, including those addressing privacy and security of records, and applicable ethics codes. [*Use this section to include very specific requirements of law. For example, in the District of Columbia, if mental health records are at issue, any release of information would have to include the following language: "The unauthorized disclosure of mental health information violates the provisions of the District of Columbia Mental Health Information Act of 1978 (§§ 7-1201.01 to 7-1207.02). Disclosures may only be made pursuant to a valid authorization by the client or as provided in title II or IV or that Act. The act provides for civil damages and criminal penalties for violations." Some jurisdictions may require that the Records Custodian specify the details of release in the patient/client record.*]

2.4 **Tracking Document**. Records custodian agrees to maintain a tracking document for disposition of any and all requests for information, which will be provided to Professional [*or Personal Representative*] upon request, as required by law.

3.0 **Compensation** [*This section should be tailored to comply with applicable law. If patients/clients are charged, there are frequently limits imposed at the state level. Also, compensation is optional and depends on the particular circumstances.*]

3.1 **Professional's/Personal Representative's Payment to Records Custodian**. In consideration of the duties undertaken by Records Custodian, Professional/Personal Representative shall pay Records Custodian [*insert agreed upon fee*] per each request of patient/client or authorized person for a copy of the records, which will cover review of records and decision regarding disposition of the request.

3.2 **Patient or Authorized Person's Payment to Records Custodian**. If permitted by applicable law, Records Custodian may charge a reasonable fee directly to the patient/client or authorized requester of records for postage and handling. [*Again, state law should be checked. Some states allow a reasonable copying fee, up to a certain limit per page, in addition to postage and handling. Other states may limit* *what can be charged to patients/clients. Fees may be different for electronic records.]*

4.0 Legal Responsibility and Insurance

4.1 **Legal Responsibility**. Each party shall be responsible for his or her own actions and omissions in connection with this agreement.

4.2 **Professional Liability Insurance**. Professional has maintained a professional liability insurance policy through [*fill in name and contact information of company*] in the amounts of [*fill in amounts, such as $1 million per occurrence and $3 million aggregate*] and will keep such coverage in effect for [*fill in time period, depending on attorney's recommendations. For example, the policy may be kept in effect for an additional 3 or 6 months after practice closure*]. Covered malpractice claims extend to the Estate of [*fill in Professional's name*]. Records custodian shall maintain his/her own professional liability insurance in the amounts of at least [*$1 million per occurrence and $3 million aggregate or other amounts*] to cover his/her own acts and omissions. Records Custodian shall not be responsible for any acts and omissions of Professional regarding treatment rendered by Professional.

5.0 Term and Termination

5.1 **Term.** The term of this Agreement shall commence on [*fill in date*] and shall extend until [*seek legal advice for specific wording, depending on exact situation*].

5.2 **Termination**. If Records Custodian ceases professional operations, or he/she cannot fulfill his/her duties under this Agreement for good cause, Records Custodian shall give ninety (90) days' written notice to Professional or Personal Representative. Records Custodian agrees to require his/her own Personal Representative and/or Records Custodian to notify Professional or Professional's Personal Representative in the event original Records Custodian becomes physically or mentally unable to perform such duties, or unable to give required notice, so that a replacement Records Custodian may be found.

6.0 Miscellaneous

6.1 **Governing Law**. This agreement shall be governed and construed in accordance with the laws of [specify jurisdiction], as well as applicable federal laws and regulations.

6.2 **Assignment**. Records Custodian shall not assign this Agreement without prior written consent of Professional, Personal Representative or his/her successor Personal Representative. Professional or Personal Representative may not assign this agreement without Records Custodian's prior written consent or without good cause, except that Personal Representative may appoint a successor in the event he/she is unable to fulfill his/her duties under the contract, due to illness, injury, disability or death. [*Seek advice from your attorney re/ wording that will apply best to your situation.*]

6.3 **Force Majeure**. Neither party shall be liable for, nor deemed to be in default for, any delay or failure to perform under this Agreement deemed to result, directly or indirectly, from Acts of God, civil or military authority, acts of public enemy, war, accidents, fires, explosions, earthquake, flood, failure of transportation, strikes or other work interruptions by either party's employees or any other cause beyond the reasonable control of either party.

6.4 **Notices**. Any notice, demand or communication required, permitted or desired to be given from one party to the other under this Agreement shall be deemed effectively given when personally delivered or mailed by prepaid, certified mail, return receipt requested, addressed as follows:

If to Professional or Personal Representative:

_____

_____

_____

Attention: [*Insert Name*]

If to Records Custodian:

_____

_____

_____

Attention: [*Insert Name*]

_____

or to such other address, and to the attention of such other person as either party may designate in writing.

6.5 **Severability**. In the event any portion of this Agreement is found to be void, illegal or unenforceable, the validity or enforceability of any other portion shall not be affected.

6.6 **Entire Agreement**. This agreement supersedes any prior agreements, promises, negotiation or representations, either oral or written, relating to the subject matter of this Agreement.

6.7 **Relationship of Parties**. It is expressly acknowledged by the parties that they are independent contracting entities and that nothing in this Agreement is intended nor shall be construed to create a principal/agent relationship or a joint venture relationship or to allow either to exercise control or direction over the manner or method by which the other transacts its business affairs or provides its usual services [*Discuss this clause with your attorney as it may not be applicable in all circumstances*].

In Witness Whereof, the parties have caused this Agreement to be executed in their names by the undersigned, who are duly authorized to do so.

Professional [*or Personal Representative*]:   Records Custodian:

_____   _____

[*Signature*]   [*Signature*]

_____   _____

[*print name and title*]   [*print name and title*]

Planned/Retirement Notice to Patients/Clients

The following is a letter that may be tailored to your circumstances when you are able to plan your retirement or other voluntary professional practice closure. You should keep evidence that such notice has been sent (e.g., return receipt, copy of letter, etc.). Check state law and/or your licensure board to ascertain whether past patients must be notified and, if so, how far back you must go (e.g., patients/clients seen within past 3 years from last date of treatment).

Sample Planned/Retirement Notice Letter to Patients/Clients

[*Keep copy in each patient's/client's chart and note method and date notice letter was sent or delivered.*]

[*Professional's Letterhead*]

[*Date*]

Dear [*name of patient/client or parent/guardian*]:

[*As we discussed during your last appointment,*] [4] I am writing to inform you that I will be retiring from the practice of [*specify profession*] [*or closing my practice*] on [*date, preferably between 3 and 6 mos. from the date of letter*]. [5] I will remain available to you until that date and will gladly work with you to make a smooth transition to a new [*specify professional, such as counselor, physician, psychologist, nurse practitioner or social worker*].

It is important that you make arrangements as soon as possible to select a new [*specify professional*]. I have listed below three [*professionals*] who have indicated they have some openings in their practices at the current time:

1)

2)

3)

[*list names, addresses and telephone numbers for each of the above*]

Timing is crucial because your new [*professional's*] practice openings and availability may change. You should contact your health insurance plan/HMO to ascertain whether you will be reimbursed for the services of any of the [*professionals*] listed above. If not, or if you prefer to obtain a referral from your health plan, the plan's staff may be able to provide you with a list of participating providers. If you are still having difficulty finding a suitable [*specify professional*], please call me and we will discuss alternatives.

If you and your new [*specify professional*] decide that my records would help provide continuity of care, you may sign an authorization to allow me to send him/her a copy of your records. [6] An authorization form is included with this letter. There will be no charge to you for providing a copy of your records if I receive your signed authorization by [*insert date; e.g., two weeks before closing of practice*] [*Following is optional language; you may want to charge a fee for all requests or delete the fee entirely*]. After this date, you will be charged [*insert fee allowed by state law*] to cover administrative expenses in copying and sending the record. [7]

Thank you for allowing me to serve as your [*specify professional*]. I have truly valued our professional relationship and wish you continued health and happiness.

Sincerely yours,

Jane Doe, [*list credentials, such as M.D., LPC, Ph.D., LICSW, etc.*]

Emergency Notice to Patients/Clients

Although similar to the planned notice letter, the language of the following template has been changed to apply in the event of emergency practice closure.

Sample Emergency Notice Letter to Patients/Clients

[*Keep copy in each patient's/client's chart and note method and date notice letter was sent or delivered.*]

[*Professional's letterhead*]

[*Date*]

Dear [*name of patient/client or parent/guardian*]:

[*As you may already know,*] [*name of professional*] is unable to continue the practice of [*fill in type of health care practice*] at this time OR has recently passed away. [8] Prior to [*professional's*] [*death/disability/illness*], (s)he designated several other [*list appropriately licensed professionals*] who may be able to establish a [*specify profession*] relationship with you or make suggestions regarding further [*treatment or other services*].

It is important that you make arrangements as soon as possible to select a new [*specify professional*]. Timing is crucial because your new [*specify professional in possessive form*] practice openings and availability may change. You should contact your health insurance plan/HMO to ascertain whether you will be reimbursed for the services of any of the [*professionals*] in the attached list. If not, or if you prefer to obtain a referral from your health plan, the plan's staff may be able to provide you with a list of participating providers.

If you and your new [*specify professional*] decide that my records would help provide continuity of care, you may sign an authorization permitting me to send a copy of your records to either you or your new [*specify professional*]. An authorization form is included with this letter. [9] There will be no charge to you for providing a copy of your records if I receive your signed authorization by [*insert date*] [*Following is optional language; you may want to charge a fee for all requests or delete the fee entirely*]. After this date, you will be charged [*insert fee allowed by state law*] to cover administrative expenses in copying and sending the record. [8] After [*specify date*], this office will be closed and the records will be sent to the records custodian, who is [*specify name, address and telephone number of records custodian if records will not be retained by person sending this notice*]. Records will be retained by [*records custodian*] for [*specify record retention period*][*if records will be transferred to a secure storage facility, you may wish to explain that this will be done but that requests to access them must be made through the records custodian*].

[*I/We*] recognize that losing your [*specify professional*] suddenly can be very stressful and hope you will consider making the transition to a new [*specify professional*].

Sincerely yours,

[Name of Professional, including credentials]

[Specify Records Custodian, Special Representative or Personal Representative]

Telephone/Voicemail Message

Sample Telephone/Voicemail Message in the Event of Professional's Death or Disability

"This is the office of *[specify professional's name]*. Due to an emergency, *[professional]* is unable to return your call. However, *[name of covering provider]*, who is covering for *[professional]*, will be handling matters in *[professional's]* absence *[OR will be answering questions and helping patients/clients make a transition to a new therapist/physician/professional]*. If you would like further information or need to schedule an appointment, please leave your name, number and a brief message and *[covering provider]* will return your call. *[Alternatively, you may leave another telephone number where the covering provider can be reached.]* Thank you."

Step–By-Step Guide to Closing a Practice

In determining appropriate members of an ERT, it is also helpful to have a clear understanding of the tasks they might be expected to take on. What follows is a list of tasks that will likely need to be completed. While an ERT might take these on in the case of an emergency, this list can also serve as a useful checklist for a professional who is retiring or selling his practice and moving into another line of work. The steps are organized roughly in order of importance. It should be noted that priorities might be different for each practice. Additionally, we do not put this forth as a comprehensive list. You may need to add particular items for your own practice.

Purchasers of this book may also download this guide from the website so that they may edit it for their own needs. http://www.privatepracticepreparedness.com/.

Note that this template is cross-referenced to the Practice Reference presented previously in the resources section. This will allow someone to readily read and work through the steps, while quickly accessing the pertinent information. For example, step one refers to "Section A", the section of the Practice Reference where the ERT information is entered.

Step-by-Step Guide to Closing a Practice

Copyright© 2014 Rob Reinhardt LPC-S, M.Ed., NCC and Anne Marie "Nancy" Wheeler, J.D. All Rights Reserved.

For Members of an ERT (Emergency Response Team): This document is intended to walk you through the process of closing the practice of a professional who is deceased or disabled. The professional who provided you with this form obtained it by purchasing the book, "Private Practice Preparedness: The Health Care Professional's Guide to Closing a Practice Due to Retirement, Death, or Disability " and may have customized it for their own practice.

This form is cross-referenced with the Practice Reference document. Where appropriate, the steps below point to the section of the Practice Reference that contains the pertinent information. This should allow you to quickly access the information necessary to close the practice.

For Purchasers of Private Practice Preparedness: Detailed instructions for using this guide are found in the companion book, "Private Practice Preparedness: The Health Care Professional's Guide to Closing a Practice Due to Retirement, Death, or Disability". You are strongly encouraged to utilize this form in conjunction with those instructions as they include important professional, legal, and ethical considerations.

Additionally, this form is cross-referenced with the Practice Reference document available to purchasers of the book. Where appropriate, steps below point to the section of the Practice Reference that contains the pertinent information. Should you make modifications to this or the Practice Reference document, be sure that the references are still accurate.

Steps to Closing The Practice of _____

1) Inform all members of Emergency Response Team (ERT) (see Practice Reference—*Section A*).

2) Identify colleagues in referral network. (Practice Reference—*Section B—Refer Patients to These Providers*).

3) Contact those colleagues to gauge ability to take on referrals. (Practice Reference—*Section B*).

4) Change voicemails and inform office staff of applicable script for answering phone calls. (Practice Reference—*Section C*).

5) Notify employees (Practice Reference—*Section D—Location of Employee Records*).

Notify employees, if any, immediately before you notify current clients. If you have the luxury of planning closure (non-emergency situations), give approximately 90 days' notice to employees and patients, if possible. Review obligations to employees, such as vacation, sick leave and other benefits. Consider keeping an administrative employee to help process records requests, etc.

6) Contact current active clients starting with those scheduled in immediate future. (Practice Reference—*Section E—Locating Active Patients*) Refer them to appropriate clinicians generated during Step 2.

7) Contact clinical supervisees (Practice Reference—*Section B—Supervisees*).

8) Contact educational institutions (Practice Reference—*Section F*).

Contact educational institutions with which the professional is affiliated. A primary example would be a university where the professional teaches classes or performs research.

9) Inform referral sources (Practice Reference—*Section B—Others in Referral Network*).

10) Inform attorney (Practice Reference—*Section B—Attorney*).

11) Inform vendors, HIPAA business associates, Internet service provider and utility companies. (Practice Reference—*Section G*).

Notify all vendors and close accounts; obtain receipts for final bills paid. Note that consideration might be given to leaving some accounts open for a brief period of time to help with dissemination of information. For example, a website might be updated to note that the practice is now closed and the office phone account may also be kept in place for a set period of time.

12) Generate and send letters to past clients. (Practice Reference—*Section E*).

Check into state law to see whether past patients must be notified. For example, some state laws require notice to clients seen within three years before date of practice closure.

13) Inform third party payers (Practice Reference—*Section H*).

14) Inform licensure boards (Practice Reference—*Section I*).

15) Inform professional associations (Practice Reference—*Section J*).

16) Inform National Provider Identifier (NPI) Enumerator (Practice Reference—*Section K*).

The National Provider Enumeration web site is: https://nppes.cms.hhs.gov. Their contact information as of this writing is:

Phone: 1-800-465-3203 (NPI Toll-Free)

Email: customerservice@npienumerator.com

Mail:

NPI Enumerator

PO Box 6059

Fargo, ND 58108-6059

17) Notify professional and business liability insurance companies (Practice Reference—*Section L*).

If professional liability insurance policy is "claims made" instead of "occurrence," obtain tail coverage.

18) Notify accountant (Practice Reference—*Section B*).

Notify accountant so that taxes are filed, to see if there are any outstanding tax issues, etc.; check contracts and make sure any appropriate cancellation notices are sent in accordance with the contracts.

19) Notify landlord (Practice Reference—*Section M*).

Check lease to ensure you may legally vacate premises without future rent obligation or may sublet premises.

20) If you are a physician, notify the Drug Enforcement Administration (DEA) and, if applicable, the state drug control agency. Arrange for disposal or transfer of controlled substances, if relevant.

21) Arrange for retention and storage of medical/mental health/business records.

22) Sell office equipment (Practice Reference—*Section D—Location of Asset Information*).

If you plan to sell your practice, seek advice from your attorney. The laws are very complex; you need to avoid fee-splitting and any violation of federal and state fraud and abuse laws.

23) Close bank accounts after all receivables are collected and invoices are paid. (Practice Reference—*Section N*).

Copyright© 2014 Rob Reinhardt LPC-S, M.Ed., NCC and Anne Marie "Nancy" Wheeler, J.D. All Rights Reserved.

Endnotes

1. "Disability Insurance Statistics," published by the Disability Insurance Resource Center. Retrieved July 2, 2013 @ http://di-resource-center.com/statistics.php.

2. See Health Insurance Portability and Accountability Act of 1996 (HIPAA), Pub. L. No. 104-191. See also HIPAA Privacy Rule, 45 C.F.R. §§ 160.101-160.312 and 45 C.F.R. §§ 164.102-164.106 and §§ 164.500-164.534 and HIPAA Security Rule, 45 C.F.R. §§ 164.302-164.318. See also Health Information Technology for Economic and Clinical Health (HITECH) Act, Title XIII of Division A and Title IV of Division B of American Recovery and Reinvestment Act of 2009 (ARRA), Pub. L. No. 111-5, 123 Stat. 226 (Feb. 17, 2009), codified at 42 U.S.C. §§300jj et seq.; §§17901 et seq. The "Omnibus Final Rule," formally called Modifications to the HIPAA Privacy, Security, Enforcement and Breach Notification Rules Under the Health Information Technology for Economic and Clinical Health Act and the Genetic Information Nondiscrimination Act; and Other Modifications to the HIPAA Rules may be found at 78 Fed. Reg. 5565 (Jan. 25, 2013).

3. Readers who are unsure of their status as HIPAA Covered Entities may consult materials put out by the Centers for Medicare and Medicaid Services. Retrieved from http://www.cms.gov/Regulations-and-Guidance/HIPAA-Administrative-Simplification/HIPAAGenInfo/AreYouaCoveredEntity.html

4. Only use this language if the opportunity presents to speak in person with the patient. This will likely apply to active clients. It is generally suggested that a notice letter of some type be sent to both active patients and those seen within at least the past two or more years. Some states may require notice to patients seen within a longer time frame. Some state licensure boards may actually consider "active" patients to be those seen within a certain period of years (e.g., 7 years),

not just those patients currently in treatment at the time a professional gives patients notice of practice closure.

5. Note to professional: if someone has been hired to take over the practice, state the following in the Sample Notice Letter to Clients: "As of [date], [name of new professional] will be taking over my practice. [Name of new professional] graduated—from [list name of school] and served at [list relevant practice experience]. You are, of course, free to seek care from any [provider] of your choice and may also wish to ask for referrals from your health plan."

6. Note to mental health professionals: specific authorization is required for release of "psychotherapy notes," as defined by HIPAA. Additionally, under some state laws, "personal notes" that are kept separate from the rest of the record should not be shared with others. Mental health providers are not required by law to keep separate psychotherapy notes or personal notes but they may provide an added level of privacy protection.

7. In most states, health care providers may charge a reasonable fee for copying records. Check with a local attorney or the state licensure board to determine what, if anything, the maximum fee is in the appropriate state. You might experience more timely patient compliance if you only charge a copying fee when records are requested after a set date, such as two weeks before actual practice closure. Also, remember that the professional or the Records Custodian must respond to valid requests for records after the date of closure and until the time period expires for retention of records.

8. Whenever feasible, it is recommended that current clients be notified by another qualified mental health professional in person or by telephone before sending written notice, so that the patient is not distraught by such a letter.

9. Note to the professional: specific authorization is required for release of "psychotherapy notes," as defined by HIPAA. Additionally, under some state laws, "personal notes" that are kept separate from the rest of the record should not be shared with others. Mental health providers are not required by law to keep separate psychotherapy notes or personal notes but they may provide an added level of privacy protection.

Annotated References

Ethics

Ethics codes are continually evolving. As you develop your policies, you should check the websites of your own professional organizations and review the applicable ethics codes. Periodically review this material. Major associations' websites are: American Association for Marriage and Family Therapy, www.aamft.org; American Counseling Association, www.counseling.org; American Medical Association, www.ama-assn.org; American Mental Health Counselors Association, www.amhca.org; American Nurses Association, www.nursingworld.org; American Osteopathic Association, www.osteopathic.org; American Podiatric Medical Association, www.apma.org; American Physical Therapy Association, www.apta.org; American Psychiatric Association, www.psych.org; American Psychological Association, www.apa.org; National Association of Social Workers, www.nasw.org. Additionally, there are various other associations, state and regional branches, and sub-specialty organizations that may have their own ethics codes or annotated versions of larger associations' codes.

Emotional and other Aspects of Retirement

Canadian Medical Association, The Non-financial Aspects of Physician Retirement; Environmental Scan & Literature Review, August 2004. Retrieved at http://www.cma.ca/multimedia/staticContent/CMA/Content_Images/Inside_cma/Physician-Health/English/pdf/Retirement-lit-summary.pdf. This article provides an interesting perspective on the emotional and other non-financial issues involved with retirement. For example, a study by the Harris County Medical Society (Canada) revealed that 27% of the physicians participating in the study showed evidence of depression in retirement; it was most acute during the first year post-retirement. Furthermore, being prepared emotionally had the greatest impact on physicians' quality of life in retirement. The study also demonstrated that health often improved with increased exercise and that more spousal relationships improved rather than deteriorated in retirement.

For a wide-ranging treatment of topics which "celebrate" aging, see http://www.eldr.com.

http://www.agelessinamerica.com is a website designed for both employers and mature workers.

Financial Aspects of Retirement

Resources abound on the various financial issues to consider. Consider Hinden, S. How to Retire Happy: The 12 Most Important Decisions You Must Make Before You Retire (4th Ed.). New York, NY: McGraw-Hill (2013). Written by a former Washington Post financial writer, this easy-to-read book focuses on both financial and non-financial decisions that must be made. It includes a discussion on Medicare, supplementary insurance and Social Security, as well as personal considerations in planning for health care needs of a spouse with Alzheimer's Disease.

Kiplinger's Retirement Report (Washington, DC), ed. Knight A. Kiplinger is a newsletter filled with financial and other retirement tips. To subscribe, visit https://www.kiplinger.com/store/krr/.

If you work for the federal government, a good resource is http://www.myfederalretirement.com.

For those interested in changing career paths or looking for new horizons in retirement, see http://www.workforce50.com.

The Coker Group, Valuing, Selling and Closing the Medical Practice. Chicago, IL: American Medical Association (2011).

Professional Will

Bradley, L.J., Hendricks, B. & Kabell, D.R. (2012). The Professional Will: An Ethical Responsibility. Retrieved from http://www.sagepublications.com. This article makes a strong case that mental health professionals should execute a "professional will" to provide continuity of client care in the event the professional therapist dies or becomes incapacitated suddenly. It includes citations to other articles on the topic, as well as a template that the reader may use.

Steiner, A., The Empty Chair: Making our absence less traumatic for everyone. New Therapist 48 (March/April 2007). Retrieved from http://psychotherapytools.com/pdf/article_emptychair.pdf.

Other Books by Anne Marie "Nancy" Wheeler, J.D

The Counselor and the Law: A Guide to Legal and Ethical Practice, Sixth Edition by Anne Marie "Nancy" Wheeler and Burt Bertram

Learn More About Rob Reinhardt

Rob is CEO of Tame Your Practice, Providing Comprehensive Consulting for Mental Health and Wellness Professionals

www.tameyourpractice.com

Phone 919.578.8263

Learn More About *Private Practice Preparedness*

www.privatepracticepreparedness.com/

Made in the USA
Columbia, SC
05 February 2022

55499314R00037